Guided Meditation for Pain Relief

*Mindfulness to Help
Physical and Mental Pain,
Take Control of Your
Depression, Anxiety,
PTSD, Addictions,
Injuries, Headaches, Back
Pain, Arthritis and More*

Positivity Protection

Table of Contents

Introduction

Welcome to *Guided Meditation for Pain Relief: Mindfulness to Help Physical and Mental Pain, Take Control of Your Depression, Anxiety, PTSD, Addictions, Injuries, Headaches, Back Pain, Arthritis, and More.* You are here to find relief at last, and this collection of mindfulness meditations and guided practices will help you control your pain, find relief, and heal your deepest issues and problems.

So many people are using prescription drugs, surgery, various therapies, and more to help relieve their pain symptoms and overcome severe addictions, injuries, trauma, and mental health issues. Often times, these practices only deal with a part of the problem, and not the whole issue. Your physical body, your mind, and everything in between also need help on the spiritual level, and as we have all learned from years of practices, dating back thousands of years, mindfulness practices, meditation, and other personal inner work practices are part of what help you heal every part of you, not just the symptoms.

You are about to embark on this wonderful audio series to help you understand how closely linked your mind and body really are, giving you the tools and the platform that you need to balance your other healing work, therapies, and medical care with powerful meditations to help you relieve chronic, sever, and traumatic issues at the core level.

If you are suffering and don't know where else to turn, you have come to the right place. Let the Positivity Protection Guided Meditation for Pain Relief help you find the healing power you are searching for. All of these meditations can be practiced individually, or you can enjoy them a few at a time. It really all depends on what your needs are at this moment.

Keep in mind that if you are in need of medical assistance, please contact your health care professional to give you aid and assistance as needed. These helpful meditations are meant to be used in collaboration with other health practices you are in need of. They are a beautiful compliment to the whole healing journey.

You will want to silence your cell phone so that you are not disturbed. Turn off the TV. Find a calm and relaxing place to meditate, and choose the most comfortable position for your body to lie, or sit in.

As you begin this journey, do not worry if you have not tried meditation before. Many people haven't. You will find right away that all you need to do is breathe and listen. That's it! We will handle the rest. So, lie back, find your comfortable space, shut off the outside world, and prepare to discover relief!

Chapter 1: Prepare Yourself for Pain Relief

This is the beginning of your new outlook on life. Your pain and suffering have come to an end, and as you begin to learn these valuable meditation tools, you will start to notice how all of your difficulties and challenges, whether they be physical, mental, or emotional, can be approached in a loving, soothing and compassionate way through mindfulness and meditation.

There are so many different ways that a person can feel pain: depression, anxiety, PTSD, addictions, injuries, headaches, back pain, arthritis, mental health disorders, recovery from surgery, cancer, and so on. Your need to relieve your pain is profound, and to help you find the right path toward recovering your strength, your health, and your personal power, you will need to begin with this simple meditation to help prepare your mind, body, and soul for what is in store.

Make sure you have found a comfortable position. If it is painful to lie on the floor or on a piece of furniture, try using pillows and bolster to prop up your knees or put under your head and neck. If lying down is too stressful on your back and hips, you can prop yourself up in whatever way feels good to you.

Try to find the best time and space to listen to this meditation so that you can fully relax and will not be disturbed.

1. Begin with your breath. Your breath is a gateway to healing and recovery. Your breath is the elixir of life that takes all of your deeper pain away, moving new oxygen through your system, moving your blood, your lymph, your cells. Inhale deeply and slowly for a count of 4 seconds, one, two, three, four, and exhale slowly for four, one, two, three, four. Good. Again. Inhale slowly, one, two, three, four, and exhale gently, one, two, three, four. Already you may be starting to feel more relaxed, more connected to your body.

2. Continue to breathe in and exhale out, recognizing your energy changing and shifting. Breathe into your abdomen first, expanding the space of your belly, pushing your navel up towards the ceiling, filling the deepest part of your body first, then filling your lungs. Exhale, letting all of the air steadily flow out of you, deflating your chest, your ribs, your stomach. Again, breathe in, pushing your diaphragm up and out, extending your belly upward gently, no need to force it, and exhale slowly out, letting your navel fall back towards your spine.

3. Continue to breathe and let the air coming into you be the healing breath of life, the life force energy that will cleanse all of your internal organs, your muscles, and tissues, your ligaments, and tendons, your cells, your blood circulation. See the air coming into you like a refreshing flush of clarity that connects to any place where you may be feeling tightness, tension, stress, stiffness, pain.

4. When you exhale, see yourself releasing all of the feelings in your body that need release, like your breath has gone through your whole system and collected anything that is stuck, anything that is stagnate, any illness or negativity, and is pushing it out as you let the air out of your lungs and abdomen.

5. Continue to breathe and let yourself fall deeper and deeper into a relaxed state. Your body carries you through your daily life. Your body works hard to lift you up, to get you out of bed in the morning, to accomplish tasks. Your body wants to feel refreshed after all that work, and your breath cycle is cleansing your internal system, from your head, all the way down to your feet.

6. When you breathe, imagine that each breath not only fills your belly and your lungs; see the fresh oxygen going all the

way down into your toes, each toe filling with the air that you breathe. Feel the air going into your head, through your sinuses, deep into your ears, your throat, your brain. Let the air fill your entire being so that you can feel relief on the deepest, cellular level.

7. As you connect to your body, your breath, your relaxation, consider how you are feeling right now. You may have some emotional stress from a difficult day. You may have a headache that won't go away. You might have some deeper pain in your body, your heart, your mind, that needs compassion and healing. Connect to these feelings right now as you continue with your breath. Listen to your thoughts, your feelings, your deeper physical sensations. Listen to your body, heart, and spirit. Inhale in for a count of four...and exhale slowly for a count of four. Continue breathing and meditate on your feelings right now at this moment.

8. [allow for a few breath cycles to pass before continuing with the script]

9. Where are you in pain? As you take air into your body, where do you have the strongest sensation? Is it in your mind? Do you sense and feel painful thoughts or memories? Is it in your emotions, in your heart center where you are feeling pain

today? Did something happen that made you feel sorrow or grief? Are you feeling pain in your physical body? Are there any wounds or injuries, any chronic issues that won't leave you be that need relief? In order to heal your pain, you need to know what it is, where it is coming from, and how it feels for you right now.

10. Breathe into your lungs, filling your torso with fresh oxygen, hold that breath for a few counts...and exhale slowly. Again, breathe in, hold, and exhale. Take a few moments to relax, breathe, and listen to what is giving you discomfort right now. Describe your discomfort in your mind. What does it feel like? Where is it in your body, your mind, your heart? How long has it been there, causing you discomfort? Do you know the cause? Continue contemplating as you connect to this energy.

11. [allow several breath cycles to pass before continuing the script]

12. Let yourself relax even further as you continue your breathing. Knowing your pain is the first step to relieving it. You can understand it more clearly and heal it more effectively when you give a name to it. Underneath all of your wounds, your history, your trauma, anything you have had to overcome both mentally and

physically, there lies an incredible power to heal yourself. You can give up any thoughts and ideas now that you will always have to feel some kind of pain. Every time you inhale deeply and exhale slowly, you are asking your healing power to make a change to your whole being. You have that power now, right here, in this safe space.

13. [allow for a few breath cycles to pass before continuing with the script]

14. You know where your pain is. You know what has caused it. Even if you don't know what has caused it, you can feel and it, and you can give it your attention right now. You can show yourself you are ready to relieve your pain. You are prepared to take control of your well-being, physically, mentally, emotionally.

15. Prepare to relieve your pain by going to where it is in your body. Let your attention and focus be with the cause or source and be present with it here as you inhale slowly. Breathe into the space where you are feeling the most discomfort. Let all of your breath go directly to this space, no matter where it is. Your knees, your low back, your hips...your heart...your memories. Breathe into the discomfort area and gently let it all go in one, slow, long exhale.

16. As your energy begins to connect more with the physical, mental, or emotional discomfort, begin to see your breath in turn into healing white light. Imagine that as you pull air into yourself with your inhale, that air has the power of light energy to flow through you and make the pain go away. See this light with your mind's eye, reaching to these spaces of discomfort or pain. Let the white, warm light completely envelop the painful space. Each time you inhale, you are filling your body with this healing light, and each time you exhale, you are letting go of your pain, your discomfort, your wounds. Just spend a moment here, visualizing this healing light flowing into you and pushing out all of the painful issues in your physical body, in your thoughts, in your feelings.

17. [allow for a few breath cycles of visualization to pass]

18. Your energy will continue to change as you feel and see this heling brightness comfort you, like a soft kind hand on your shoulder, like the perfect medicine and remedy to your unique pain and discomfort. Enjoy the sensation of being full of light instead of dark shadows. Your pain will be cleansed and relieved when you perceive this energy through your thoughts. To prepare to relieve your pain

and heal your deeper issues, you can simply visualize the healing occurring on a deeper level. Use your mind, your thoughts, your breath, to instinctively and intuitively go to the source of your discomfort, whatever it is, wherever it is; however, it may be feeling right now, and see it changing.

19. Your power to heal yourself in this way is strong. You have the power to look at your healing journey in a new way. Acknowledging your pain is the first step to relieving it. Trust yourself. You know how to heal your own wounds. You have all of the answers locked deep inside of you. Whenever you need instant pain relief or a way to prepare for further healing meditations, remember to use your breath and breathe light into your body, your mind, and thoughts, your heart, and emotions, everywhere you can picture going, you can send healing to yourself, through yourself, through your thoughts, through your breath.

20. Let go of any belief that your pain is a part of your identity, or that it won't go away, or that it is too hard to heal. None of these things are true. You have everything you need to prepare for pain relief. Always begin and end with a healing breath. Inhale slowly, filling your abdomen, your chest, your skull, filling your arms and

hands, your thighs, your legs, your toes. Pause for a moment before you exhale, slowly letting go of anything that feels uncomfortable, anything that feels rough. Melt your pain away with another deep breath in and hold for a moment, now exhale gently, slowly. Breathe here for a while, visualizing white healing light, focusing on all spaces within you that need relief. Breathe in light, let out discomfort. May you feel rejuvenated and refreshed, relaxed and calm, soothed, and loved.

21. [allow time and perhaps soothing music for the end of the meditation]

Chapter 2: Full Body Tension and Breath Relaxation

Your body carries a lot of pressure, be it emotional and mental pressure, or physical pressure. Every day, you sit, stand, walk, lie down, communicate, accomplish, attend to life, with whatever your body is carrying, with whatever discomfort you have gotten used to over time and have learned to live with. Sometimes, we stop noticing the pain until it gets so advanced, we have to stop and do something about it.

Meditation to release full-body tension is an excellent way to prevent yourself from getting to that breaking point. Using this meditation on a daily or weekly basis will help you check in on all levels with your body, what needs attention, and where you have been ignoring yourself. You can use it in the morning before starting your day or at the end of the day when you need to release everything that has built up over the course of your daily life.

For the best results, especially if you are someone who has chronic discomfort, use this meditation daily to help you attend to the deeper matters for a while, finding a bigger, broader way to keep your physical body, as well as your mind, from building up too much pressure over time. See it as part of your healing regimen, to connect with your tension daily, or weekly, to fully release and remind yourself how good it feels to be loose, relaxed, and in a state of comfort.

Make sure you have found a comfortable position. If it is painful to lie on the floor or on a piece of furniture, try using pillows and bolsters to prop up your knees or put under your head and neck. If lying down is too stressful on your back and hips, you can prop yourself up in whatever way feels good to you.

Try to find the best time and space to listen to this meditation so that you can fully relax and will not be disturbed.

1. Listen to your breathing. Are you breathing deeply enough? Focus on the breath of your inhale pouring in through your nose and pushing your abdomen out. Feel your diaphragm extending and pulling your lungs open to feel the fullness fo the oxygen you are breathing. When you cannot breathe in anymore, hold the breath steady for a few moments...and now gently, steadily, begin to exhale, controlling the release of air so that it takes time to let it all out. [pause for exhaling] And again, take a long, slow breath in, pushing your navel toward the ceiling, feeling your lungs expanding outward, pulling fresh oxygen fully into your body. Hold the breath calmly and

connect to the sensation of feeling full of this breath. [pause for a moment] And finally, release the breath very slowly, controlling the release, letting it drain, like air leaving a balloon, slowly seeping out and deflating your chest and abdomen.

2. This is the breath of deep calm. You can always use this slow breath cycle to help you relax, to relieve your muscles and tissues of tightness, to calm and soothe your thoughts and your feelings. Slowly take air in once again, trying to pull it into you over a count of ten seconds...hold the breath in for a count of five...and release for a count of ten.

3. [allow 30 seconds for the listener to practice this breath cycle]

4. You are now more relaxed and connected to your body. If you need to make any adjustments to your posture, to the way you are positioned to feel more comfortable, do so now. You are here to release tension fully form your body, your mind, your spirit. You are here to listen to the energy inside of you that needs comfort, that needs relief. You can continue to breathe normally while you begin to relax into your wholeness and feel your body sink more deeply into relaxation.

5. [allow a brief pause for relaxation]

6. Begin to focus on your feet. Notice how your feet are feeling right now. Have you walked a long road today? Do you feel the pressure of standing all day long or the burden of carrying weight in your feet? How do you carry yourself on your feet? Does it feel stable and grounded here, or wobbly, painful, sore? Focus on the energy you feel in each toe...in the ball of each foot, in the arch, the heel. Spend time considering how much your feet really do for you every day, how far they carry you, how long you stand on them.

7. Take a long, slow breath in, breathing all the way down into each foot, filling the space with your breath. Hold the breath for a moment...and slowly exhale all of the tension out of each toe, the top of your foot, the arch, the heel, everywhere you feel the pressure of daily life. And take another deep breath in, slowly filling your feet with healing energy. Hold here for a moment...and gently release the tension from your feet as you exhale out.

8. [pause for a moment of meditation]

9. Notice the feeling in your ankles, connecting your feet to your legs. You may want to roll them a little in gentle circles; you may want to just keep them still.

Notice the feeling in your calves and your shins. Do you feel tightness here? Can you feel the pressure of your posture in these muscles? Notice what your ankles and your calves feel like, your shins, your whole lower leg. Breathe in gently and deeply, sending healing oxygen to these places, circulating air through your delicate ankle bones, up into your calves, around your shins. Hold the breath here for a moment and then gently exhale out all of the tension held in these strong muscles. And again, inhale deeply, pulling fresh air and healing energy into your ankles and lower legs, pause...and exhale all of the tension out.

10. [pause for a moment of meditation]

11. Connect to the feeling in your knees. Your knees bear a lot of weight; they help you walk forward. They help you walk up and down the stairs. What do your knees feel like today? Are they stiff, sore, tight? Do you feel the pain of too much standing or sitting in your knees? Can you sense the tension in this space? Take a nice long inhale, filling your knee cavity with new lightness. Breathe into the space of your knees and hold the breath here for a moment...and exhale slowly, soothing your knee joints as you release the tension. And once again, inhale deeply into your knees, holding the breath in here

for a few moments, pulling relief into this large joint...and slowly release all of the tightness and stiffness from this space.

12. [pause for a moment of meditation]

13. Moving up further into your upper legs, above your knees, concentrate on your thighs, your hip joints. Feel the powerful energy of your quadriceps and your hamstrings. Notice any tension you feel in these large muscle bellies. Feel where your thighs connect to your pelvis. What do your hips feel like? Do they rotate easily? Are they stiff from sitting down for long periods of time? Are they loose and movable, or tight and stuck? When you take your next deep breath in, pull all of your air into your thighs and hip joints. See the space light up with fresh air. Hold your deep breath for a moment's pause...and exhale slowly. Again, breathe new healing energy all the way down into your thighs, extending down to the knee, filling the whole upper leg and hip joints with fresh oxygenated blood. Pause for a moment...and release all of the tension here.

14. All of your lower body, your hips, thighs, knees, your calves, ankles, and feet, are now fully relaxed. You have released the tension with deep, soothing breaths in and exhales out.

15. [pause for a moment of meditation]

16. Working your way up the body, concentrate on your pelvic bowl, your tailbone, your lower vertebrae. How does your low back feel, the top of your hips, the space between your lower ribs and your pelvic bones? What tension are you carrying here? Can you bend in the middle, or is too stiff, too tight? Notice the feeling of this area, where your upper and lower body meets. Focus on pulling healing life force energy into this midway place in your body as you inhale deeply, filling your low back, pelvis, sacral area, and tailbone, with fresh air and light. Feel the air connect to any tightness or tension here as you hold the breath in for a moment...and slowly release the breath out, blowing away all of the tension. Again, pull air into your low back, your pelvis, your sacrum, hold the air here, and breathe it out.

17. [allow for a moment of meditation]

18. Moving up along your spine, focus on your whole torso, from the top of your ribs, down to your navel. Notice any feelings you may have here. This is the space that carries almost all of your organs, your digestive system, your heart, your kidneys, and bladder. How does the length of your

spine feel? Strong? Achy? DO you feel like you have to work hard to stand up straight? Notice all of the tension in your torso and connect again to your breath. Take a nice deep inhale, pulling new oxygen into your lungs and abdomen. Slowly fill your whole torso with air...hold it here...and slowly release all of the stiffness you are carrying here, sinking more deeply into the floor or the chair you are in. Breathe in again, felling the whole center of your body becoming lighter, freer, more open...as you hold the breath, relax into this sensation of clarity in your organs and spine...and let it all out in one, strong exhale.

19. [pause for a moment of meditation and release]

20. Your whole body, from the top of your ribs, down into your toes, is free of tension. With your next breath in, concentrate on your arms, your upper extremities. Focus on your whole shoulder complex, from the shoulder blades, around to the front of the shoulder and down into the arms, the elbow, the wrist. Notice how you feel in the palm of your hands, in your thumbs, and your fingers. What kind of work do your hands do? What do your arms and shoulders have to lift? As you consider the feelings in your arms, enjoy a slow and deep breath in,

filling the entire length of your arm, through your fingertips and up into your shoulders, with your breath. Hold here for a moment...and release the breath out, letting go of all of the tension you carry here. Take another soothing breath in...hold it...and release it out, freeing your shoulders, your elbows, your wrists from tension. Feel the tightness in every finger bone and joint just melt away.

21. [allow for a moment of meditation and release]

22. All of your body is relaxed up to the neck. Take a moment to feel the weight of your relaxation sinking into the floor. Scan your entire body, from the feet, up through your shoulders and arms, and see if there are any spots of tension if you are holding onto anything still so that you can release it all of the way. Take a breath in, very slowly, filling the whole space of you below the throat. Hold here for a few moments. And slowly release the breath, melting fully into the floor.

23. [allow a moment before moving forward]

24. Concentrate on your upper spine, your neck, your cervical vertebrae. Feel where your shoulders meet your neck. Feel where the top of your spine connects to your skull. Are you holding any tension in

your cheeks, in your lips, in your ears? Are you holding onto anything in your jaw muscles, in your forehead and eyebrows, in the muscles on top of your head? Feel the energy of your whole head, your neck, your throat. Find any deeper tension, and worry you carry in your face or jaw, all of the cares you carry in your neck. Bring your next deep breath into your head and neck. Slowly inhale healing energy into this space and feel all of your cares melt away from your neck, your facial muscles, your jaw. Feel all of your doubts and fears leave you as you exhale slowly out. Inhale in...hold here, filling your neck, throat, jaw, brain, with fresh oxygen...and release it all out of you, fully releasing all of the tension of your thoughts, your mind, your emotions.

25. [allow a moment of meditation and release]

26. Your entire body has now become fully relaxed. You are free of tension, from your head to your toes. Scan your body in your mind again. Can you feel any tension anywhere? Are you still holding onto something that you need to let go of? Take a moment to breathe into any remaining areas of tension that you may have, releasing them fully so that you can be totally relaxed and relieved.

27. [allow for a few breath cycles to pass]

28. You can continue to lie or sit in this space, feeling the total relaxation of your body and your mind. Spend time existing in this state of being. Enjoy the feeling of freedom in your body and know that you can release tension anytime you need to in just a few short minutes of meditation, using your breath to bring relief from your head to your toes. Just breathe here for a time before moving forward with your day. May you feel rejuvenated and refreshed, relaxed and calm, soothed, and loved.

29. [allow for a space of soothing music for the listener to enjoy a space of peaceful, tension-free relaxation]

Chapter 3: The Mind-Body Connection Meditation

Your healing journey starts with the Mind-Body Connection. You are here to understand how to let yourself find the fullness of healthy and pain-free living by opening your world to the power of positive thoughts and mindfulness meditation practices. It is ancient wisdom that your thoughts and feelings become a physical experience; that all of your pain, wounds, trauma, griefs, and sorrows can be held, trapped, and repressed in every cell in your body.

You may not even realize it, but you can even have a significant physical reaction to a negative encounter with another person, or situation. All of our daily experiences can have a positive or negative impact on our thoughts, our minds, our general beliefs, and attitudes, and yes, it all forms as a physical reaction or wound in the body.

Your doctor is probably not going to tell you this, but your entire human anatomy is closely linked to your energetic frequency, the ethereal matter so often called the spirit by so many different cultures. This meditation aims to help you bring together the link between your thoughts, emotions, your energy, and the physical body that carries it all.

You can begin to truly heal all forms of injury, trauma, repressed emotions, chronic pain symptoms, issues from PTSD, anxiety, and depression, all of it, with a simple guided meditation to help you connect your mind and your body, showing you how easy it is to heal from the inside out. The mind-Body connection is powerful. If you think that you will never heal, then you will believe it is true. If you think you can heal yourself, then you will.

Make sure you have found a comfortable position. If it is painful to lie on the floor or on a piece of furniture, try using pillows and bolsters to prop up your knees or put under your head and neck. If lying down is too stressful on your back and hips, you can prop yourself up in whatever way feels good to you.

Try to find the best time and space to listen to this meditation so that you can fully relax and will not be disturbed.

1. Open your mind to relaxation. Feel yourself floating on a raft in the middle of the ocean. You are safe. There is nothing around you. Just water. It is comforting to be gently rocked on this soft raft. The sun is not too hot. It feels warm and gently soothing. You are being lulled by the soft ripple of waving water under your body. You can sense that there is only water around you. There is no land in sight in any direction, but you feel safe to just rest, knowing that you are not lost at sea; you are simply resting and enjoying the

soothing rhythm of the waving water and the warmth of the sun.

2. [allow a moment for visualization before continuing the script]

3. You are now going to take a few moments to connect more fully to your thoughts in this space. You are alone in on the raft, no other person in sight, no land, no ships. There is nothing but you and this raft. You can sense that the ocean is beneath your back, deep and endless. It is as vast as outer space. You can feel the power of this great depth underneath you. How does it feel? Do you remain calm? Are you able to continue enjoying the imagery of lying on the raft in the glow of the sun reflecting on the water like diamonds? Are you able to feel soothed in this place? How does it feel in your body when you sense that there is nothing but a raft between you and miles of endless, deep ocean?

4. [allow for a moment of meditation and reflection]

5. If you are feeling uneasy at this point, don't worry. You are safe. Now, imagine that you are back in your room, wherever your body is lying down or sitting for this meditation. You are comfortable here. It is familiar and safe. Did you notice during your visualization any particular physical

feelings? Any emotions about the quality of the experience? Were you fearful or uncomfortable pretending to be adrift at sea? Did you clench any muscles in your body as a reaction to protect yourself? Or did you feel excited in your body, about the giant life force in your mind, imagining the power of the ocean next to your body? What was your reaction in your body, in your mind, in your feelings?

6. [allow for a moment of reflection before moving forward]

7. To understand how your mind affects your body and how your body affects your mind, look at this perception of reality. You were not really on a raft at sea, all alone. You were not in danger at any moment. Your thoughts can perceive danger, even when it isn't real. Your emotions and thoughts can tell your body how to feel. Take a deep breath in, filling your entire being with fresh air...hold your breath for just a moment...and release it fully, pushing away anything that feels stuck, right now at this moment. And again, inhale deeply, filling your entire body...hold it steady...and exhale slowly and gently.

8. Return your body and mind to that raft floating on the ocean waves, rippling quietly, lapping against the sides of the

raft. You are here to heal in this space. You are here to heal the places in your thoughts that you are connecting to your physical self. You are here to heal your physical pain with positivity and mindfulness. You are gently rocking in this raft and are floating slowly toward a shoreline. You can feel the edge of the land bump gently against the side of your raft. You are grounded here and can safely lie on the raft, soothed by the flowing water beneath you, tethered to the earth.

9. [allow for space for visualization before continuing]

10. The sun is comfortably warm and healing. You will not burn in the sun; you will only feel its healing light and golden brilliance. Your body is resting here. Your thoughts are free to perform the healing you need. It doesn't matter where you need healing. It could be anything, anywhere in your whole being. It is about connecting your mind with your body and your body with your mind. Focus on the energy of your breathing. Draw your breath in and notice how it causes a change, not just to the way you feel physically, but also how you feel mentally. Notice the humming and vibration of being soothed by your own breath. Continue to see yourself gently rocked by the water on your raft in the warm sun. You are not floating away. You

are safely tied to the shore. You can just be here and breathe, feeling how your thoughts change, feeling how your body is changing.

11. [allow a few breath cycles to pass before continuing]

12. Where are you feeling discomfort? In your memories? In your thoughts about your career, your home life, your relationships? In your joints and muscles? Where is your mind trying to tell you to look as you lie here, floating on the soothing stream of water? What is your body communicating to you without words or thoughts? What ideas and images continue to come forward in your mind? Are there any deeper feelings or emotions you might be pushing against? Take a few moments to gather your thoughts and meditate here. Keep your breath deep and slow, controlled inhales, and exhales.

13. [give pause for a few breath cycles before moving forward]

14. You might not have a fully clear idea of how your mind and body are asking you to focus. You will always find the truest answers when you let all of your thoughts be heard; when you let your body tell you where you need the most love and compassion, when you give way to your

deeper feelings, whether they are good or bad.

15. Concentrate on your image of being afloat. There is a long rope connecting your raft with the shore. As you become more aware of what your mind and body want to heal from the inside out, the rope stretches you back out to sea. You are safe to float away from the soil of the shore and connect more deeply to your unconscious thoughts and feelings. The ocean beneath represents your subconscious mind. Everything hidden is below the surface of the water. As you float further out on the calm and quiet waves, gently rocking you, you can connect more deeply to your mind-body connection.

16. [allow a few moments for visualization and meditation]

17. Staying focused in your thoughts and the image of yourself floating on this raft, tied to a distant shore, let any images, repressed feelings, memories, a stream of consciousness, ideas, and mental thoughts come to the surface from deep underwater. Carefully listen to what comes up. Do not reject it. Do not avoid it. Just let it float up to you where you are. Let it connect to you and your raft, floating in the water.

18. [allow for several moments of visualization to pass before continuing]

19. What has come to the surface? Your first response will often be the best choice for meditation. Let your intuition guide you. If you have it in your thoughts now, hold it here. If you haven't found it yet, don't worry. Just keep floating on your raft, and it will come. Connect to the image, the idea, the memory, whatever shows up for you, and hold it here in this space. Let it fill you up. Don't be afraid to see it in your mind's eye. If it feels negative or painful, you may try to push it away or ignore it. Try not to avoid it if you can.

20. [allow for a moment of meditation]

21. Now, where are you feeling this though in your body? Where in your whole body are you feeling anything tense, tight, painful? Do you have any feelings that weren't there before? Your mind has brought up an important idea or thought for you to face, and now you are going to discover where you connect to it in your body. Is it in the soles of your feet? Your neck and back? Do you feel it in your knees or your hips, or at the base of your skull? When you find the physical feeling in your body, connect to it fully, and take a deep breath in and exhale slowly out.

22. [allow for several moments of reflection and meditation before continuing]

23. This is where you open the door to healing this thought or feeling in your body. When you struggle with pain, grief, negative emotions, you will hide it in specific places in your body; in your shoulders and back, in your thighs, in your ankles and feet. It can be anywhere. When you spend time in meditation, focusing on these ideas, feelings, thoughts, and memories, you can find the source of where it connects to your body.

24. You can learn the same from your body. Where you are feeling pain right now is connected to an emotion, and belief, and attitude. When you look at this powerful connection when you find the true source of these painful experiences, moments, injuries, wounds, you can heal them at the core; you can heal them for good.

25. To continue supporting your deeper healing within the Mind-Body Connection, practice this helpful guided meditation every day for one week and observe how noticeable different you feel. Notice how much stronger, more energized, and how much calmer and more relaxed you feel in general. The powerful connection between the body and mind is not to be taken for granted. If you have experienced any kind

of trauma, emotional distress, panic attacks, serious injury, chronic illness, and more, then this meditation will be a wonderful way for you to go directly to your source and heal from deep within. May you feel rejuvenated and refreshed, relaxed and calm, soothed, and loved.

Chapter 4: Visualization for Uncovering Your Pain

Now that you know more about the Mind-Body Connection from the last meditation, you can go even deeper into your subconscious mind and body in order to repair old wounds that are emotional and physical. Uncovering your pain can be a long process, so don't expect to have everything resolved after meditating once or twice. Healing is an ongoing journey that will take a lot of patience.

You can uncover your pain by using your knowledge and understanding of how powerful the mind-body connection truly is. If you haven't already, trey listing to Section 3 to prepare you for this slightly more advanced, deeper wound healing meditation. Remember, your healing is in your hands, and in order for you to see and feel the results of your recovery, you have to regularly use these tools to help you make the healing progress you so deeply desire.

Make sure you have found a comfortable position. If it is painful to lie on the floor or on a piece of furniture, try using pillows and bolster to prop up your knees or put under your head and neck. If lying down is too stressful on your back and hips, you can prop yourself up in whatever way feels good to you.

Try to find the best time and space to listen to this meditation so that you can fully relax and will not be disturbed.

1. Prepare to let go and step away from the outside world. Prepare your body, your mind, your heart, and your soul to finally let go, release, and restore your well-being. Take a few deep breaths and settle into the position you have chosen to be most comfortable for you. Connect to your breath and make any adjustments that you need to so you can feel fully relaxed and settled.

2. Welcome to a new healing path. Welcome to uncovering your pain. You are just getting started with learning and knowing to trust your own intuition, your own body, your own mind, to show you the way, to help you heal, to find relief from old wounds, trauma, depression, and anxiety. After you have become fully settled in a relaxed pose, you can now begin to go deeper into your subconscious layers deeper into the cells that make up your entire body and finally uncover the source of your pain and sorrow.

3. Take a moment to ask yourself a few questions: how are you feeling right now? What do you think you need to heal or resolve? Are you listening to your thoughts, your emotions, and your body to

tell you what you need? Inhale deeply and reflect on these questions for a moment as you exhale slowly. Breathe for a few cycles and connect to how you are feeling right now in this moment. Be honest with yourself. There is no need to hide anything. Let the truth of your pain come up to the surface to be heard.

4. [allow for a few breath cycles to pass before continuing]

5. Now that you have done an assessment of how you feel, now try to answer the following questions for yourself: how would you like to feel? What are you going to like about your new feelings? What does your intuition tell you would be a good choice or a healthy path to help you make this change in your feelings, in your comfort levels, in your mental and physical health? Inhale deeply again and exhale slowly out. Spend some more time breathing slowly, reflecting on these questions. Answer intuitively for yourself how you would like to be feeling at the end of this meditation.

6. [allow for a few breath cycles to pass before continuing]

7. Wonderful. Continue to embrace the calming effect of your breath and the soothing experience of connecting to your

wants and needs. Listen to what you are telling yourself on a deeper layer. Listen to how you are responding to these questions and thoughts. Now it is time to go further, deeper into your unconscious reality. Inhale deeply again and prepare to visualize what your pain is and why it is here.

8. [give a moments pause for preparation and reflection]

9. Imagine yourself standing next to a well of water. As you lean over and look down into the well, you try to find the bottom. You can only see blackness. You reach down on the ground and pick up a small stone, reaching it out over the opening of the well and dropping it in the opening. You watch and wait to see if there will be a splash in the bottom of the well, on the water's surface. The journey down seems endless as if minutes are passing. As if the well has no bottom at all and is just a portal to another dimension.

10. [allow a pause for reflection and visualization]

11. You can see no bottom to the well, and as soon as you realize that it is endless, you begin to feel pulled inside of the well. At first, you feel as if you are falling. But then you quickly realize you have the feeling of

floating on air. You are not falling. You are being lightly pulled down into the well, which no longer feels like going down...it is looking forward. As you enter into this portal, take a deep breath in and let yourself succumb to the pull forward into another dimension.

12. [allow for a few moments of breathing and visualization]

13. As you slowly embark on this mysterious journey, you notice that the darkness of this portal begins to lighten. Rays of soft, colorful light are moving through this space. It begins to look more like a tunnel to another world. The lights are showing you the dimensions of the portal. It is big enough for your body to pass through it without touching any of the walls. As you float forward, the lights changing their glow through each color of the rainbow, you begin to wonder if the tunnel will ever end. You wonder where it leads to, and why you were even going on this journey in the first place.

14. In this never-ending tunnel, you begin to feel centered and calm. There is nothing outside of this space, and you will continue traveling through it until you discover why you are here. You are here to uncover your pain. How does your pain look to you now in this space? What kind

of pain is it? Is it emotional? Mental? Physical? Are you suffering from something specific, or is it something broader? Float through this endless expanse of timelessness and reflect again on why it is you are here. What are you trying to uncover and resolve today?

15. [allow for several breath cycles to pass before continuing]

16. Are you ready to uncover it more? When you know what it is you are here to uncover, you have to look deeper. That is only the beginning. Continue to inhale and exhale deeply, slowly, while you imagine yourself floating in this ethereal portal with no end. Begin to ask about your pain. How long have you had this pain? When did it first begin? Was there another pain before it that was similar? Think about your discomfort in this way. You are uncovering clues about your feelings, your thoughts, your body, like a detective, searching your inner world and subconscious self for information to solve the mystery.

17. [give a few moments of space for reflection and visualization]

18. You can keep floating forward in this light-changing tunnel, gaining more speed as you get a little closer to uncovering your

pain. As you move further along, connect to it again and ask yourself why the pain is still present. Why has this pain not been resolved yet? What has prevented you from helping yourself heal from it?

19. [allow for several moments of reflection to pass]

20. Concentrate on all of the details now. Is there anything missing from your discovery? Have you answered all of your questions about it? Do you feel like you are able to understand it better? Do you know how to resolve it? Take a few deep breaths in and release them slowly as you reflect on this in your light tunnel...

21. [allow for a few breath cycles to pass before continuing]

22. Now you are coming closer to an endpoint in the tunnel. You have started to see a light at the end of it, like a pinpoint of brightness, far, far away. You have only to keep moving forward in order to reach the end of this journey of healing and recovery. Whatever your pain may be, somewhere on the physical layer, and emotional pain, a deep trauma-however, it manifests for you, you are here in this tunnel of powerful healing light to uncover what it is so you can heal it more and more.

23. The light at the end of the tunnel is slightly bigger now. As you move toward it, the lights reflecting all around you in the tunnel walls are getting brighter and bolder in color. With every shift of light and color going through the tunnel, it is now beaming directly into you from all sides of the tunnel walls. You are completely surrounded in red light...now orange...and yellow...green...now blue...indigo...now purple-violet light...you are now bathed in silver light...and golden light...finally, the light is pure white. It is almost blinding as you pass forward through the opening at the end of the tunnel. You are held here in this pure white, light space. Continue to visualize this powerful light surrounding you as you breathe deeply for several cycles.

24. This light is piercing through your pain. Every color of light that passed through you in the tunnel has helped you to heal on every layer of your being. You are held by light as it dissolves everything that you discovered in the portal, everything that you uncovered about your pain, your wounds, your hurt. Let this bright light hold you and heal your wounds.

25. [allow a few breath cycles before continuing]

26. You have opened up your unconscious mind to uncover your pain on a deeper layer. Some pain is the result of childhood memories or experiences. Other pain is from accidents or unexpected health scares. It can be only in the mind or heart, the center of your emotions. Listen to the messages you get from your higher self, from your deeper wisdom, from the pain itself. You are an intuitive being made of pure light, and if you are able to discover the deepest moments of what has caused you to feel wounded, harmed, or afraid, then you will know what to do to heal and resolve it.

27. Take a few moments to breathe clearly, deeply, slowly. Reconnect to the physical space that you are in. You are no longer in the tunnel. The light has returned to normal. You are in your room. You are safe. You have traveled deeply past the world and into your deeper dimensions of information and truth.

28. Take some time after you are ready to return to normal life to reflect on your discoveries. Spend time contemplating what you have shown yourself here in this tunnel of light. You will always discover something new, every time you reach into the bottomless well to uncover your deeper truths. Practice this meditation often to help resolve the deepest issues.

May you feel rejuvenated and refreshed,
relaxed and calm, soothed, and loved.

Chapter 5: Meditation for Mental/Emotional Pain Relief

Not all pain is physical. There are ways that your mind can create pain in your body, or that your sadness and grief cause you to feel achiness or physical weakness. The mind-body connection is so strong that even if you think your low back pain is the result of bad posture, it can also represent a deeper emotional wound or trauma.

For many of us, our physical pain is more obvious, easier to take care of or remedy, and has a way of telling you very quickly that you need to pay attention to it. Mental and emotional pain can look healthy on the surface, but underneath the ocean of the mind, there lies a deep, unacknowledged pain.

Mental/Emotional pain can come from not knowing how to process your feelings or experiences. It can also be the result of challenging or difficult relationships, starting as early as infancy. It can be from traumatic situations that are completely out of your control. There are many versions of what causes or creates mental and emotional pain for every individual.

This meditation is designed to focus more on that part of you, the part where you may bury your feelings, or neglect the deeper issues. Your physical body can certainly bear the brunt of what is hurting you mentally without you even knowing. Relieving the emotions that caused you pain can also change the way your body feels overall.

For this meditation, prepare your heart and mind to travel more deeply into your emotions, your beliefs, the attitudes you have about yourself. Prepare to unravel and unfold the painful parts of your psyche that keep you locked in pain. If you find this activity challenging, don't worry. You can always return to it when you are feeling more open to this kind of deep, emotional work.

This guided meditation is intended to be as relaxing as it is healing and impactful. Make sure you have found a comfortable position. If it is painful to lie on the floor or on a piece of furniture, try using pillows and bolster to prop up your knees or put under your head and neck. If lying down is too stressful on your back and hips, you can prop yourself up in whatever way feels good to you.

Try to find the best time and space to listen to this meditation so that you can fully relax and will not be disturbed.

1. Begin with your breath. Enjoy a refreshing deep breath in through your nose, keeping your inhale slow and steady. When you inhale, try to push your navel upward,

filling the abdomen, then the lungs, breathing out rather than up. Exhale slowly, steadily releasing your breath until you are fully empty. And again, inhale slowly through the nose, pulling in as much air as you can, as slowly as you can, and exhale for the same amount of time. Let your body feel the change that comes from healthy breaths. Your breath is healing. It is a natural way to reconnect with your mind, your body, your spirit.

2. Take a few moments to enjoy a few breath cycles with this slow and steady inhale and exhale pattern. Let yourself dissolve and refresh from within, with every breath you take, with every exhale you make.

3. [allow for a few breath cycles to pass before continuing]

4. Your body is free to melt into the place where you are lying or sitting. You don't need to hold onto anything from your daily life right now. There is nothing you need to think about, nothing you need to do. There are no accomplishments, goals, or tasks that need your attention. All that is needed is for you to relax in this space. All you need to do is breathe, and with every exhale, feel yourself go deeper and deeper into a state of peace. Peace of mind, peace of heart, peace in your physical body.

5. As you relax more deeply here, give yourself a loving thought. You work so hard to do what you can to make your life work. You live to the best of your ability. You are allowed to make mistakes, to lose control, you are allowed to take time in your day to meditate and teach yourself how to heal. You have permission to grow, to relax, to find what it is that you need the most, and give it to yourself. You may want to think of a simple affirmation on your mind to help you feel this self-compassion. Something that simply says, "I am worthy of this time." "I am worthy of love." "I am worthy of healing and feeling well." Take a moment to breathe and repeat some loving thoughts in your mind as you inhale deeply, and exhale slowly.

6. [allow for a few breath cycles to pass before continuing]

7. There is nothing to worry about, nothing to fear. You have the time to spend taking good care of yourself. You have the ability to offer yourself what you need better than anyone else can. You are connected to your deeper actions for healing. Listen to your intuition. Trust that you are already doing what you can to make progress, to relieve your stresses and worries, to relieve any sorrows or hidden pains. Trust

that you will heal as long as you are open to connecting with yourself in that way.

8. With your body more relaxed, you can focus more on your mind, your thoughts, your emotions. You can focus on your memories, your childhood, your relationships with others. Your energy is dependent upon finding the truth of who you are and what lies beneath. Your truth is more important right now than anyone else's. Don't worry what other people say, how other people make life work, or how they tell you you should do it. This isn't about anyone but you. If you find yourself wondering about someone else's perspective or beliefs, reconnect to your own with a deep inhale, finding your center once again. Trust that you know the difference between your true feelings and someone else's.

9. [allow for a pause for reflection]

10. Just relax and listen. All you have to do is listen. You don't have to overthink. There are no right or wrong answers. There is nothing to prove here. This space is for you to know yourself more deeply, to identify the parts of you that are hidden, that may be unresolved. You are solving the puzzle of yourself, and you can find all of the pieces that you need, right here, inside of you. The puzzle pieces are

nowhere else, but here within you. All you have to do is listen to yourself. All you have to do is allow whatever is below the surface to come up for resolve, no matter what it is, no matter how painful it may seem. Try to look at it, even if you are afraid. You are safe. You have nothing to fear. You are protected by these words, by your own body and mind. You are free to look at where you are stuck, trapped, blocked, hurting. Your wounds need your love and guidance through this process. Your hurts need your help by looking and seeing what they are right now. Spend a few moments with your breath, and just listen to your inner thoughts. Notice anything that comes up right away. Notice anything that you might try to avoid seeing or feeling. Let yourself naturally come to it as you breathe slowly, deeply.

11. [allow for a few breath cycles to pass before proceeding]

12. Where did your mind take you? What are your feelings right now? Are they good? Do they feel negative or painful? Is it something you already think about all of the time, or is it something you have worked hard to forget, to ignore? Your past is where you learned how to feel, how to live life, how to look at yourself. Your past is when your hurts became wounds that wanted healing at that moment, but

may never have been fully resolved. Your earliest childhood memories can be the source of your deepest sorrow, and you may not even know it yet. If you are having any difficulty hearing your thoughts or letting your memories and emotions come to the surface, don't worry. It can take some practice if you are used to keeping things buried underground. Try to let yourself relax more fully so that you can bring into the light that which aches to be known.

13. [allow for a pause for reflection]

14. Now that you have had some space to reflect, what are you going to do with these thoughts? These ideas? These feelings or memories? Where do you go from here? Give yourself a moment to hold the thought or feeling clearly in your mind. Define it. Clarify it. Did you have an experience that was painful? Is there a person in your life that made you feel unworthy of love? Is there a place where you hold onto all of your old hopes and dreams, but never let them out of you, never let them become more than just a dream? Take a moment to refine your thoughts and feelings. Make it clear what it is that has come up. Know yourself within this moment.

15. [allow space for reflection and meditation]

16. Ask yourself a question about this specific idea or moment: why did it hurt? Why did this cause me pain? What happened to me in this situation, with this person, with this experience, with this part of me, that made me feel wounded or hurt? Hear your intuition answer these questions. Try not to reject the true answer to these questions. You already know the answer, locked deep inside. Answering these questions is where you begin to heal the pain. When you know why you know how. Why did it hurt? Why did it cause you pain? What happened to you that made you feel wounded, unsafe, rejected, fearful? Take a moment to just breathe into these questions and let your mind naturally come to the answer.

17. [allow for a few breath cycles of contemplation]

18. If you don't come up with an answer right away, don't worry. The point of this guided meditation is to help you create awareness around your deeper wounds and hurts that exist in your mind and emotions. All you have to do is begin to see, begin to ask these questions. The answers will inevitably come. If you feel you have an answer, then you are in a good position to release the trauma or the

pain of that moment. You can heal this place inside of you very simply.

19. First, begin with another deep breath in, holding the breath when your chest is full for just a moment, and exhale slowly out. Again, inhale deeply into the abdomen and lungs, holding the breath for a moment, before you steadily exhale out.

20. Bring your focus to the thought you came to. Bring your focus to the 'why': why it caused you pain, why it hurt you. How has it affected your life to feel this pain? How has it created your identity? How have you lived your life because of this hurt?

21. [allow for a few moments of reflection before moving on]

22. However, this pain has hurt you; this wound has caused you long-term discomfort; it is now time to let it go. It is time to move forward and release it from your identity, your experience, your deeper, unconscious thoughts and beliefs about yourself. It is time for you to love yourself instead of holding this wound within you. Give yourself what you need in order to be free of this pain. Acknowledge your worthiness for healing and recovery again. Acknowledge your right to love yourself, no matter what happened. Make it your mantra to overcome this hurt: "I

am worthy of this healing moment. I can give myself the loving words I need to release this wound. I am ready to be free of this now. I release it with all of my heart."

23. Repeat this mantra again in your mind: "I am worthy of this healing moment. I can give myself the loving words I need to release this wound. I am ready to be free of this now. I release it with all of my heart."

24. Take a slow deep breath in, hold it for just a moment or two, and now release it fully, breathing out the pain you had stored in your mind and emotions. Again, breathe in deeply, holding that breath for two counts, and release it fully, exhaling your worry, your doubt, your fear.

25. You can repeat this mantra, or something like it, throughout your day. The more you acknowledge your experience, the more you acknowledge the why and the how underneath your surface, the more healing you will find, the more resolve you will feel, the freer your mind and heart will be to be truer to yourself.

26. Come back to your breathing again and prepare to return to your regularly scheduled life. Let yourself process these feelings and emotions naturally. You may

have a lot of feelings on top of the surface after this meditation, and that is normal. It is normal that you will have some thoughts and feelings stirred up. That is the point of healing these trapped wounds. They need light to be healed. Let them be in the light of day with you so that you can heal the past and the present, to make way for a more harmonious future. May you feel rejuvenated and refreshed, relaxed and calm, soothed, and loved.

Chapter 6: Practicing Processing Pain

Pain cannot be avoided, especially if it is causing you to put your life on hold, or is having a negative impact on your ability to live a normal life. It can be frustrating, upsetting, and difficult. The reality of pain is that it is a powerful signal to let you know when something is not right. It doesn't have to be physical pain. Emotional suffering and mental disturbances are just other ways for you to acknowledge different kinds of pain that can be experienced by every human being.

To resolve pain, it is a process of patience with an end goal of full recovery. You can choose not to process your pain and live a long life of discomfort, or you can face what the pain is and learn from it how it will be best resolved. Not all pain can be relieved on your own, and you may need medical advice or care. You can use this guided meditation to use in addition to any other form of assistance or therapy you need for your personal situation.

Your journey through the pain is half the battle. This guided visualization process won't last forever and is intended for repetitive use to help you process your specific pain, no matter what it may be. After you have used it a couple of times, you may not even need to listen to it. You can just close your eyes, wherever you are, and transport yourself to a place within where you can mentally, emotionally, physically, and spiritually process your personal experiences.

In order to prepare for this meditation, find a comfortable position. If it is painful to lie on the floor or on a piece of furniture. You may want to use pillows and bolsters to prop up your knees or put under your head and neck. If lying down is too stressful on your back and hips, you can prop yourself up in whatever way feels good to you. You can also use this meditation anywhere you need to, so don't worry if you have to sit up in a chair at the doctor's office while you wait for your appointment.

1. Close your eyes and focus on your breath. Make sure your breath is coming in through your nose and out through your nose. If you are congested, you can modify your breathing. Take a breath in, taking it slowly, steadily filling up your lungs. Breath into your navel so that your belly extends as you breath in, expanding your diaphragm and opening your lungs more fully and effectively. Exhale slowly, controlling the release and letting the airflow out as steadily as it came in.

2. Again, take a deep breath in, inhaling slowly and smoothly, filling your torso with fresh air, enriching your blood and muscles, and exhale slowly, breathing out your tensions, your worries, your

concerns. This time, when you inhale fully, hold your breath for a count of five seconds, keeping your lungs fill as you count. And release the breath slowly through your nose. Again, inhale, taking in as much air as you can, hold the breath for one, two, three, for, five, and steadily release the breath, slowly deflating your lungs.

3. Continue to breathe deeply. Your body has become more relaxed. Your breath has stabilized you, grounded you, refreshed your brain, your blood, your muscles. You are here to relax and restore your body. Your body can let go of more now as you continue your deep breathing. Give up the world outside. Give up your obligations, your responsibilities. Give up your worries and cares. Give it all to your exhale. Breathe it all out of you and let free your mind for other matters.

4. [allow space for meditation and breathing]

5. Imagine that you are surrounded by a bright, golden light as if you are inside a bubble or an egg. You are in the center of the light as it completely wraps around you in a soothing and calming way. The golden color feels warm like rays from the sun. It covers your entire being and gives you the safety and protection that you

need while you are feeling vulnerable. Let it completely surround you.

6. As you sit in this glowing capsule of light, continue breathing steadily and smoothly, feeling the pleasure of this relaxed space. Where are you feeling pain in here? Is it in your body, your limbs, your organs, your muscles? Is it in your feelings, in your heart, in your mind? Does it feel as strong as it did as when you first began this meditation? Connect to feeling your entire being inside of this golden light space.

7. [allow for several moments of breathing and reflection]

8. Your worries and cares are dissolving inside of this golden light. Your pain can dissolve here too. Relax into your breath, keeping it steady and deep as you continue to visualize this light around you. Begin to see this golden, amber light permeating your skin, passing into the deeper layers of your epidermis, down to the layers of muscles, tissues, ligaments, tendons, filling all of these spaces with this liquid, honey light.

9. [allow a moment for reflection and visualization]

10. See the golden light penetrating your organs, your bones, your blood vessels.

See it coursing through your veins like blood, waking up every part of you with healing light and life force. How is your body feeling right now? How is your mind, your thoughts? How are your sensitivities, your emotions, your heartfelt cares, and worries? How do they feel bathed in this golden light?

11. [allow a moment of reflection before moving forward]

12. Going deeper now, looking more deeply into the spaces where your pain lives, can you see it in your mind? Can you visualize what your discomfort feels like? Does it have a shape, a texture, a color? If you could hold it in your hand, would it feel heavy or light, soft or sharp? Get an idea in your mind of the pain you have. Give it a shape and texture. Give it a physical form that represents the way it feels inside of you.

13. [pause for visualization and reflection]

14. With the form of the pain in your mind, notice where it exists. Is it where you are feeling physical pain? Does it overtake a larger part of your body? Is it tucked far away, deep in your mind? Can you sense and feel it in your heart? Notice the space where you see and feel this pain the most.

See the shape of it there. Feel it take up space here, with its texture and weight.

15. [allow a moment for visualization and reflection]

16. As you continue your focus in this way, keep your breath steady and remain bathed in the healing light that surrounds you as you meditate. Continue to stay centered in this space, breathing gently and slowly. Hold the form and shape of that pain; however, it looks and feels to you on the inside. As you continue this visualization, start to notice the golden light inside of you and surrounding you becoming a soft, healing, violet light. This is the color of light now circulating in your bloodstream, in your bones and tissues, in your many layers. Let the violet light become even brighter as it surrounds the form of the pain you visualized in your mind. Send the violet light directly into this shape. See the light enter the shape and cover it with healing vibrations.

17. [allow a moment for visualization and reflection]

18. If your pain feels resistant to this healing light entering it, try changing the color within it. Make the light a darker purple, or a brilliant blue. Sending an emerald green healing light into the shape of your

pain. Find the right color of light to penetrate. All of the colors of the rainbow might be the best remedy for you. Remember, there is no right or wrong with your internal healing process. Let yourself intuitively find the right way.

19. [allow for a moment of visualization]

20. When you have found the right vibration of color and light to heal this form of pain, begin to see the pain transform. Notice that its shape is altering, or that its size is shrinking. Visualize the shape getting smaller and smaller. Feel it becoming lighter and lighter as it shrinks in size. The pain is shrinking. It is evolving into something else. See, it get smaller and smaller until it disappears. Watch it evaporate in the colorful light penetrating it. If it doesn't completely shrink away, try zapping it with a bright ray of that golden light that you started with. Process the pain with light. Penetrate whatever remains of the original shape with the brightest, biggest light you can imagine.

21. [allow a moment's pause for visualization.]

22. Take a deep, soothing breath in. As you inhale, see the light within you and surrounding your return to the golden hue from the beginning. Cover yourself in a

soft, warm blanket of this light and feel a new sense of powerful, healing energy. Connect to your whole body, your thoughts, your feelings at this moment, as you continue with your deep breaths in and slowly exhale out. How are you feeling now? How is the pain you were feeling? Can you still see any remnants of that shape and form you processed? Can you feel it? Listen to your body, your thoughts, your energy. Pay attention to what is there now.

23. If you are still in pain, try performing this same meditation again on the same wound or injury, painful thought, or idea. When you go back, notice how the shape of it has altered after one meditation. Notice how it is already different from what it was before. Processing your pain is possible when you are ready to let it go when you are ready to see it change. If you are ready to eliminate your pain, then you are ready to watch it dissolve and disappear from within. You are in control of your pain, and you have the power to transform it.

24. Reconnect with your breath again and let your body feel the harmony you have created at your core from this guided visualization. Inhale deeply into your abdomen and chest, breathing in the golden light that surrounds you. Every

time you inhale, you are pulling in the orb of light around your body, breathing in its healing power. When you exhale, you only release any lingering pain. The golden light stays inside of you. Inhale again, pulling in the soft, warm light, letting it fill your entire being. Exhale your concerns, your doubts, your worries, feeling a full release of processed pain.

25. Inhale golden light until it is no longer surrounding you, it is inside of you. Exhale any negative thoughts, ideas, emotions, keeping the golden light within your being. Your body will hold the power of this healing, golden life force energy throughout the day. Remember that it is within you. Picture it there when you are feeling any discomfort, anxiety, worry, or fear. You are safe within this golden light. You are able to relax within it. Inhale, the last bits of golden light into your lungs, filling your body, all the way down to your toes, through your fingers, into your skull. Exhale the last pieces of discomfort left over from before. Breath out your stress. Let it all go with breath and healing light within.

26. [allow space for visualization and breathing-several breath cycles]

27. You are now ready to face whatever comes next. Continue to visualize this process of

pain relief as often as you need it. You can do this anywhere, anytime you need relief. May you feel rejuvenated and refreshed, relaxed and calm, soothed, and loved.

Chapter 7: Unlocking and Unblocking Patterns of Pain

There are times in life when your cycles and challenges feel like they are never-ending. You might say, "I am always like this," or "I never seem to get over this." These ideas, these concepts, these thought patterns are beliefs created by the mind that keep you locked in cycles of pain. You can resolve these painful patterns, unblocking and unlocking them so that they can be transformed into more positive healing frequencies.

Over time, your mind will just naturally think in more positive directions, instead of staying in patterns of grief, sorrow, depression, or feeling like it is impossible to overcome any physical ailments or chronic conditions. Your beliefs affect your body, your attitudes, and your emotions. If you believe that you are "always" going to have pain, then you will. If you believe that you deserve to feel bad, then you will convince yourself that there is no alternative.

Thought patterns, emotional cycles, physical practices that keep your body out of healthy alignment, all of these things can be resolved when you create mindfulness around the patterns first, and then learn to replace them with more positive outlooks and healing beliefs.

To prepare for this meditation, make sure you have found a comfortable position. If it is painful to lie on the floor or on a piece of furniture, try using pillows and bolsters to prop up your knees or put under your head and neck. If lying down is too stressful on your back and hips, you can prop yourself up in whatever way feels good to you.

Try to find the best time and space to listen to this meditation so that you can fully relax and will not be disturbed.

1. Connect to your body in the position you have chosen to relax in. Take a few moments to make any adjustments to help yourself feel totally comfortable and at peace with your position.

2. As you find the right placement for your body, honor that you have come here to do the healing work necessary to relieve your pain and suffering. You are taking control of your health and wellness. You are giving yourself the love and attention you deserve. You are taking time to be present with yourself at this moment, to embrace your deeper consciousness, to embrace your fullness, and your wholeness. You are preparing to take better care of your mind, your body, your spirit. You are here to awaken a new pathway to healing yourself.

3. Take a deep breath in, inhaling through the nose, slowly, controlling the flow and

keeping it nice and steady. Bring all of the oxygen into your lungs that you comfortably can before you exhale fully, releasing all of the breath and letting go of the cares of the world around you. Breathe in again, letting your mind and body know that you are here to relax and restore your health and well-being. Exhale softly, controlling the release, letting it leave your body gently.

4. Practice opening your mind to the healing power of your breath. Open your mind to letting out all of your stress and concerns with every breath out. Use your creative thoughts to imagine that you are breathing in healing light with every inhale, filling the space within you with more of the energy you desire to feel today. Let go of your ideas or beliefs that it isn't possible to heal in this way. Let go of any parts of you that feel resistant to loving yourself through this healing practice.

5. [allow a few breath cycles to pass before moving forward]

6. You are more deeply connected to your body, to your intentions, to your powerful healing thoughts and mentality. You are ready to go deeper into your beliefs about your body, about your reality, about who you are as a person. You are ready to begin

knowing what lies behind your attitudes and cycles of thought, the beliefs that keep you on a certain path, the thoughts that mold your existence. You are here to break through the outworn beliefs and issues that keep you locked in pain.

7. Your body can feel all of the harsh words you speak to it. Your body holds onto any negative attitudes you have about yourself, about the life you are living, about whether you are good enough, strong enough, successful enough. Your beliefs and thoughts carry through your entire physical structure and are resolved to stay there. You already know that you can heal these wounds and patterns. You already know that deep down, below the surface, you are more powerful than your thoughts, then the words you think about yourself, about your abilities, about your strength.

8. Take a deep, soothing breath in through your nose and connect to this power. As you exhale, take a moment to think about your body. Think about how you feel about your body. What words come to the surface? What thoughts do you have when asked to look at your body, to consider the size, the shape, the health of it, the age, the flexibility? Where are your thoughts trained to go when you think about your body?

9. [allow for several moments of reflection]

10. Listen to the pattern. Acknowledge what that pattern might be, or where it might come from. It might just be one simple word. It could be several sentences. Notice what feelings come up when you think this kind of thought. Notice how your energy might change or become lower or more negative, or positive and more open. Connect to your breathing as you acknowledge your train of thought about your body. Acknowledge what kinds of words or phrases come forward in your mind. If they are negative ideas, then you are unlocking what needs to change. If they are negative ideas and beliefs about your ability to heal, your ability to handle your work or family, or your ability to feel beautiful, then you are blocked from feeling the way that would make you the happiest, the most whole, the freest to live as your true self.

11. If your thoughts say something like, "My body is weak," or "my body never heals quickly enough," now is the time to change that belief. Here you begin to unblock your pain so that you can feel ready to heal it so that you feel welcome to try. Here you get to change the patterns of your mind to help you instead of hurt you. Now you get to say, "I am strong. My body

is strong." You get to say, "my body heals as fast as it needs to. My body is already healing, right now, at this moment." Take a few moments to practice a new thought pattern. Change the words and beliefs. Show yourself that you value your body. Teach yourself to think in new ways, pushing through the pain you have believed in, pushing through toward the outcome you desire.

12. [allow for a few breath cycles for reflection]

13. You are opening a new door to healing and recovery. You are unblocking your pain and giving it a new attitude. If you believe your body is capable of healing, if you believe that you are beautiful, if you believe that you can change the way you feel, then you can. Then you will. Your thoughts tell you what to feel. Your feelings tell you what to think. Your beliefs shape who you are and govern your existence. Changing your patterns of pain changes your beliefs about that pain. Listen to your wise, inner voice tell you what you already know: you are capable of wholeness. You are enough. You have everything you need within you to transform. You are worthy of love and giving love to yourself. You are here to unblock the pain that holds you back. You deserve to feel well again.

14. [allow for space for meditation on this point]

15. You are ready to go even further through this process. You can see what it feels like to change your thought patterns, your beliefs. You can feel what it would be like to know this all of the time, this new way of seeing yourself and your journey. Connect to your breath and sink more deeply into your relaxation. Give yourself time to open up to your new thought. Bring this thought back up and repeat it to yourself every day. To truly change your beliefs about your body, about your ability to heal and be strong, you have to spend time focusing on your new beliefs about yourself. This is an affirmation. It is the sacred mantra of your healing path. Hold it close to you. Do not let it evaporate away. Give it solid ground in your life every time you wake up in the morning, every time you begin to doubt yourself. Show yourself what you want to think about, not what you are used to thinking about.

16. Take a long, slow breath in, inhaling the satisfaction of knowing that you are making a small change, a small change that leads to bigger changes on your journey ahead. Exhale away your old thought pattern about yourself. Fully

release that idea with your slow breath out and show yourself that it is gone, that this thought doesn't belong inside of your mind anymore. Connect to this breathing and meditation for a few moments, inhaling your new beliefs, exhaling the old, outworn attitudes you have carried about your body.

17. [allow for several moments of meditation and reflection]

18. You are getting closer to unblocking your pain and unlocking new thoughts and ideas, new beliefs, and attitudes to help you make a greater change from the inside out. It all begins from your consciousness. Listen to your mind again. Let your thoughts naturally evolve and take shape as you breathe in and exhale slowly.

19. [allow for some time for reflection]

20. Your mind is always full of information, always working something out, always thinking, dreaming, making associations. Let your mind associate freely for a few moments. Let it travel around from one place to the next. Let yourself just mentally exist until you can begin to notice a thought pattern. What information does your mind keep focusing on? What thoughts are you going back to over and over again? Can you identify it?

21. [allow for several moments of meditation and free association]

22. If you haven't arrived at a pattern of thinking yet, do not worry. You are beginning to train your mind to make these observations. It comes with practice. You can find yourself going off into other places, or drifting off into deep relaxation for a while. If you have a pattern of thought you have discovered, hold it in your mind. Connect to the thought. If it is more than one thought, observe how they are linked together. What is the common thread between these patterns? How are they related?

23. [allow for some moments of reflection]

24. As you gain a better understanding of your thought pattern, try to become more detailed and specific about it. Help yourself work through the cause of these thoughts, or how long you may have been thinking them. You can ease into identifying it. Sometimes it may be too intense or too much information to unravel in one meditation. The point is to create awareness of your thoughts so that you know how to change them.

25. As you did in the last thought meditation, find a way to make the thought more

positive. Restructure the thought to become something else, something that helps you to grow and heal, rather than something that creates obstacles, or holds you back. Your choice to think a certain way can now change into something else. You can choose to think more specifically about your healing. You can choose to change your self-deprecating thoughts through a new affirmation, a new belief about yourself, your work, your life. Take a few moments to inhale, bring in slow, deep, soothing breaths in, changing your thought pattern into something better, stronger, healthier. Exhale all of the negative attitude and belief patterns that keep you from growing that keep you from feeling whole.

26. [allow for several moments to pass for meditation]

27. Inhale deeply again, and repeat your new mantra or affirmation in your mind. Feel the relief of knowing that you have just changed a belief that you have the power to choose a healthier way of thinking and feeling. You are able to resolve your pain in this way. By changing your thoughts, you change your beliefs, the way you feel, your body, everything.

28. Practice this meditation frequently to continue transforming your outdated,

outworn thought patterns. Empower yourself to choose new ways of thinking, new ways of healing, and new ways of taking control of your life. As you move forward in your day from here, remind yourself regularly of your new thoughts and ideas. Keep them solidly in your mind. Practice thinking them so that they remain with you, replacing your negative beliefs completely. May you feel rejuvenated and refreshed, relaxed and calm, soothed, and loved.

Chapter 8: Mindfulness Meditation to Heal the Body

Mindfulness is a powerful form of meditation. It can be practiced in every part of your life. You don't have to be lying down in a quiet room in order to enjoy mindfulness. It will be useful throughout the day during a variety of activities. The aim of mindfulness is that you are fully present within each moment. To be mindful is to acknowledge what 'is' right now.

You can begin this meditation anywhere you want. It helps if you are in a situation where you will not be easily disturbed. Once you become more skilled with practicing mindfulness throughout your whole day, it won't matter if you are disturbed during your meditation. You will just be ready in the moment for whatever comes.

1. With your eyes closed, let yourself feel your breath. Calmly enjoy the sensation of how it feels to take air in through your nostrils. Feel what it is like when your lungs expand. Enjoy the sensation of getting fresh air into your body. When you exhale, let yourself mindfully feel the relief of deflating your lungs, of letting go of everything that you just pulled into you.

2. Steady your breathing to your normal, comfortable breath pace. Take note of where your resting breath is. Be mindful

of where your breath feels the most relaxed and normal.

3. [allow for a few moments of mindfulness]

4. Take a moment now to scan your whole body. If you want your eyes to come to an opened position, you are welcome to soften your lids to an opened look. You may feel that it is easier to "see" how your body feels with your eyes closed.

5. Go through your body, one area at a time, starting at the top of your head, and working your way down to your toes. Notice every tiny sensation, every detail of how your body is feeling. This is mindfulness. Mindfully acknowledge everything you can about how your body feels right now, at this moment in time.

6. [allow for several moments to pass for the body scan to be completed]

7. Whatever you have come across in your physical body, you are now more aware than before of how it feels. Feel free to describe it in your mind in ways that are meaningful to you. For example, you might think that your neck feels like it is full of small pebbles and stones and that you want it to feel smooth and malleable, like soft clay. Another example: you can notice that your chest feels thick or

stagnate like it is full of cotton candy that is hard to breathe through and that you would prefer it to feel like a soft, wet fog on a cool morning. Be expressive. Mindfulness means you are able to more deeply connect with your true feeling within the moment. Feel it with a thoughtful description.

8. [allow for several moments of mindfulness meditation]

9. You are even more aware of your body than before. You are mindful of what feels good, what feels bad, and what feels like nothing in particular right now. Take another relaxing breath in, and slowly exhale, releasing the feelings you have from that imagery. Open your mind to another layer of mindfulness. Go to the place in your body that felt the most uncomfortable. Find the spot where you felt the deepest discomfort or pain. Spend a moment longer connecting to this part of your physical form.

10. [allow for a moment of physical connection]

11. With this space now open again, remind yourself of how you described this feeling. Contemplate how you would specifically describe this feeling mindfully. Inhale

deeply and meditate on this sensation for a few moments.

12. [allow for a moment of reflection]

13. Notice what would happen if you changed your posture slightly, or found another position to lie, stand, or sit in. It is okay to move your body right now. Mindfully approach your physical body in this way. Connect to it by acknowledging what would help to make it feel different. Perhaps you intuitively find a specific stretch that feels right at the moment, or you may have found a better posture or position for your body that affects what you are feeling.

14. After you have made this change, mindfully observe how long it takes for the sensation to return, how long it takes for you to feel that discomfort again. Notice if it feels the same as it did before you shifted. Notice anything new that has occurred because of your shift. Observe if there are new places that have grown in discomfort as a result of this change that you have made.

15. [allow for several moments of reflection and meditation]

16. Give into your specific sensation. If you have discovered something new about it,

change the way you are describing it. The purpose of mindfulness is to be fully present within every moment. You are creating deeper awareness with your body, which is the source of total healing and recovery. Breathe deeply and reflect on these new sensations, describing them in new ways. Make any adjustments you need to in order to feel your body transform. You may need to change your position again or enter into another stretch of some kind. Your intuition will guide you through what is needed within the moment.

17. [allow for several moments of adjustment and mindfulness]

18. Return to your breath again. Focus on filling your lungs slowly with new, fresh oxygen. Hold the breath for two seconds before releasing your breath in a steady exhale. Again, notice how it feels as you breathe in slowly, taking in the soothing new oxygen-rich breath, hold for a moment, and exhale slowly and smoothly.

19. Connect to your body again. Scan your whole physical form, from head to toe, looking for anything new, any changes from when you originally began this meditation. Focus on where you are feeling the most intense sensations. Be present in the moment and attend to the

most obvious feelings. When you find the part of your body that needs your mindful approach, connect to it with your breath, inhaling into it, and exhaling away from it.

20. It might be the same place as before. It might be somewhere new. Stay present in the moment and describe how it feels in your mind. Notice every detail. Notice every thought or feeling that becomes associated with it as you contemplate this area of your body.

21. [allow for several moments of meditation]

22. This part of your body is asking you for something. Show yourself what it is. It could be a change of position, shifting your physical body. It might be a specific stretch that feels best. It may also be a visualization. Your body may want you to visualize the change in your feeling from within. You can imagine yourself surrounded by colorful light, healing the space where you are feeling discomfort. You may find that an affirmation or mantra feels the most soothing at this moment. Relax into it and allow your intuition to show you. Trust your body that it knows what it needs right now. Mindfully evoke the right action to relieve this space and take a moment to perform that action.

23. [allow a moment for action to be performed]

24. Take a deep breath in, noticing every detail of how it feels to inhale into your lungs. Notice the feeling of oxygen filling your body. Feel the sensation of release, focusing on the specific feelings that are connected to an exhale. This is mindfulness.

25. Take a few breaths in this way, fully connected to every part of the breathing experience. Relax into it and let your body inform you of any new information. Carefully listen to all of the signals, the cues, the information that your body is reporting to you as you breathe in and out.

26. [allow time for breathing and reflection]

27. You are now aware of how to practice mindfulness in its simplest form. This is something we all forget to do, to be aware of, to explore. So many of us are living slightly in the past or future, and less frequently in the moment. You will be able to heal yourself more powerfully and effectively if you can trust yourself at any moment in time. All you need is focus, concentration, and the guidance of your breath and intuition, and you can experience life more fully and wholly.

28. Trust your mindful mind to carry you for you to show your discomfort and how to heal it in the moment. Trust yourself to live fully in the present so that you can feel 'here' now. May you feel rejuvenated and refreshed, relaxed and calm, soothed, and loved.

Chapter 9: Believing in Your Healing Ability Through the Mind and Soul

If you have practiced any of the other meditations in this audio, then you have already learned that your beliefs are powerful, and they impact your ability to heal fully. If you believe something is impossible, then it will be for you. If you believe you have the potential to recover fully from any of your issues, illnesses, emotions, and so on, then you will have a greater ability to move forward in that direction and will likely heal more quickly as a result.

This guided meditation is a simple way to help yourself feel empowered to heal and relieve any pain that you may be suffering through your beliefs. You are already everything you need to be on this journey. All you need to do is believe that no matter how deep the wounds, no matter how long the suffering, no matter what the doctors tell you about your progress, your beliefs affect your ability to heal and transform.

For this meditation, find a comfortable position to relax. If it is painful to lie on the floor or on a piece of furniture, try using pillows and bolster to prop up your knees or put under your head and neck. If lying down is too stressful on your back and hips, you can prop yourself up in whatever way feels good to you. You can also sit up in a chair or other furniture it feels easiest for you.

Try to find the best time and space to listen to this meditation so that you can fully relax and will not be disturbed.

1. Begin with healing breath. Bring a full breath of air deep within you. Hold it here. Exhale the breath and connect to your mediation state. Let go of your cares and concerns. Release your doubts and fears. There is nothing to worry about in this space, at this moment. You are safe.

2. Calm your mind and body by continuing to breathe slowly and deeply, filling your chest with soothing, healing breaths, exhaling them fully, pushing out anything that is causing you stress or anxiety. Enjoy the pleasure of every breath cycle and connect to a deeper state of mindful relaxation.

3. [allow for several breath cycles and relaxation period]

4. You are here at this moment to transform your mind. You are here to open your beliefs, your attitudes, your thoughts, and feelings, to have the life you want to live, to be the whole person you desire to become. You are here to embrace the truth of your story with recovery, with trauma,

with deeper wounds. Your story is important, and it deserves space in this world. You are here to let yourself find an opening for healing and growth. You are here to transform.

5. [allow a few moments for reflection and meditation]

6. You have the power to succeed on your journey. You have the willpower to make it happen right now. You are willing to spend your time and energy to honor your need to recover, to heal, to make a bigger change inside and outside of yourself. You are the only one who knows what it truly feels like deep down inside. You are the only one who really knows how it has felt for you to go through what you have gone through. Your path belongs to you. Your healing belongs to you, too.

7. Take a deep breath in and honor this truth. Take a few moments to really honor your experiences, your sorrows, your grief. Find space within you to acknowledge that it has been hard, that it has felt endless. That you have needed more than you have been able to give yourself along the way. Take some deep, soothing breaths as you meditate on your healing work and your journey.

8. [allow space for reflection and meditation]

9. You are going to heal, no matter what has happened in the past. You are going to heal, no matter what you have thought before. You are your own healer, and you know the right spiritual medicine to get through this time in your life. You have all of the answers deep inside of you. All you have to do is trust your inner guidance. You are going to get through this. You have all of the energy that you need to take care of yourself in this moment. You have the power to feel good again, to understand what has happened. You have the power to feel successful in your healing process. You have the patience to get through to the other side. Take a few moments to connect to your breathing. Meditate on your healing power as you slowly inhale and exhale.

10. [allow for a few breath cycles and mediation to occur]

11. Your healing path may have been long, or it may have just begun. It doesn't matter where you are on the journey. You are here, now, and you have a beautiful, joyful, vibrant life to live. You have so many things to do and enjoy. You have a wonderful purpose here in this life, on this Earth, even if you don't know what it is yet. Right now, your purpose is to believe that you can heal from the pain you have

suffered. Your purpose is to tenderly hold yourself in this space and share your love with your hurt moments, your wounds, your injuries. Your purpose is to find the right healing path for yourself, knowing that it won't be exactly like everyone else's.

12. Your beliefs impact your healing process. If you believe you can't, you won't. If you believe you can, you will. If you believe that it won't work for you, then it will not be what you are hoping for. If you believe that you have the power to heal, no matter what has happened, no matter how long it has been, then you will continue to find growth and success on your path.

13. The power of positive healing is in your thoughts, your beliefs, your heart, your soul. Your heart has always known the right way to heal. Listen to your heart. Let your heart influence your thoughts. Let your heart love your process and become more available to the changes that come when you say 'yes' to recovery and relief when you say 'yes, I can heal.'

14. Connect to your breathing again and reflect on these thoughts and words. Reflect on opening your heart to guide you and your belief in yourself.

15. [allow for several moments of reflection, meditation and breathing]

16. Once you have gained some sense of power with your healing thoughts and ideas, think for a moment what they were before you began this meditation. How were they different? How were they the same? Can you feel a difference in your mind, in your heart? Are you feeling a greater sense of empowerment about your journey through your recovery and relief?

17. When you are ready to open your eyes and gaze around the space you are sitting in. Take a few deep breaths to open and awaken after your affirmations and empowering meditation. You are here, right now, learning as you go. You don't have to have everything figured out right now. All you have to do is trust yourself that you have what it takes to get through this. You have what it takes to overcome your painful struggles, your addictions, your anxiety, or depression. You have what it takes to forgive yourself from the time it took to get here. All of us grow differently, at different speeds, with different belief systems. Here and now, with your eyes wide open, you have the power to see into your future. You can do this. You are already doing this. And you are already successful because you are here, now, listening to this empowering meditation to push you even further.

18. Take a deep, relaxing breath in, filling your lungs all the way to capacity. Hold your breath here for a moment, and gently exhale. Again, inhale deeply into your lungs, hold it, and exhale slowly. Good.

19. You are now ready to move forward on your path. Whenever you feel doubt, fear, worry, pain, and you need a little push forward, use this audio meditation to remind you of how powerful and capable you are. You have everything you need to relieve your pain and suffering. All you need to do is believe it. May you feel rejuvenated and refreshed, relaxed and calm, soothed, and loved.

Chapter 10: Awakening to Your Healing Path

Your healing path may be long and difficult. It may go back all the way to your early childhood development, or traumatic experiences in your youth. Your healing path may be the result of struggling with substance abuse and working through addictions, or it may be related to emotional pain from abuse or challenging relationship dynamics. The healing journey can also be about recovering from chronic illness and disease, or from emergency surgery.

There are a number of ways that pain will manifest in each individual's life, and so for every one of these meditations, you will have your own unique experience with how it helps you, how you see it in your mind, and what the results will be. The more frequently you connect to yourself and your healing path through these guided meditations, the more quickly you will find a sense of calm, peace of mind, and relief from your pain and suffering, whatever it may be.

This final meditation is a simple, reflective, soothing a relaxing way for you to feel awakened to your healing journey. It may not always be easy, but it is worth it, and the more you practice opening your healing pathway, the faster you will find the relief you are looking for.

Find a comfortable posture or position to sit or lie down. If it is painful to lie on the floor or on a piece of furniture, try using pillows and bolsters to prop up your knees or put under your head and neck. If lying down is too stressful on your back and hips, you can prop yourself up in whatever way feels good to you.

Try to find the best time and space to listen to this meditation so that you can fully relax and will not be disturbed.

1. Spend a few moments adjusting your position, making sure you feel relaxed where you are most comfortable. Silence your devices. Turn off the outside world. You are here to practice aligning with your energy and acknowledging your healing path.

2. Connect to your body for a few moments. Simply engage with your breathing, relaxing into it. Try not to overthink it or worry about the timing of it. Just breathe. Give yourself a moment to feel your body sinking more deeply into a relaxed state as you breathe. Enjoy the feeling of letting go and releasing everything you have to worry about in your daily life. Release all of the tasks, the meetings, the to-do lists. Let go of the problems you might be having with any people in your life. Let go of the morning or afternoon traffic, the emails, the voicemails. Let it all just fall

away as you feel your body and your breath.

3. [allow for several breath cycles and meditation space]

4. Going deeper into your mind and body, feel any places that are carrying tension. Listen to your body. Feel any spaces where you might be clenching your muscles, like your jaw, your neck and shoulders, your hips. Take a moment to breathe out all of the muscle tension you have been carrying around with you for a while. Let it fall away from you like you are dropping a big sack of potatoes on the floor, with every exhale of breath.

5. [allow for a few breath cycles and meditation to pass]

6. Every day when you wake up, you are on your personal healing journey. Every morning, when you feel the start of a new day, a new beginning, you have a choice to make about how you want to get through the day. It begins with your belief that you are willing to do what it takes to go on this path.

7. Imagine you are lying on your back in a field of flowers. Every possible color is present on this hillside. You don't need to worry about being anywhere or doing

anything for anyone else. you just need to be present here, on this hillside, surrounded by colorful flowers.

8. After a moment of reflection here, you decide to get up and look around. You see, a path stretched out in front of you. It seems to begin exactly where your body is lying in the flower field. This is the beginning of your day. It starts right here and now. Take a deep breath and imagine yourself setting off on this path. See your journey beginning with a step forward into new territory.

9. [allow for a few moments of visualization and reflection]

10. As you get further down this path, what is the first thing you have to deal with as you begin a new day? What is in your path? Is it a friend, a colleague, a family member? Is it a challenge or something that you are afraid of doing? Show yourself what it is. Acknowledge it. If it is someone you care about, give them a hug and a kiss goodbye as you set off further in your day. If it is something you are afraid of or something you don't want to face, look at it straight on and acknowledge it here. Let it know you are aware of it. When you look at it straight on, then you will no longer be afraid of it or dislike that it is there. Ask it to step aside so that you can move on.

11. [allow for a few moments of visualization and reflection]

12. Moving down your path again, what shows up next? What obstacles do you have to face next on your journey? Be specific. Follow the same format as before. If it is someone or something that you love, honor it with love in return. If it is something painful, disturbing, upsetting, or annoying. Look at it square in the face. Know what it looks like. Know what your obstacles are. If it doesn't move out of your way, speak directly to it. Tell it why you don't like it. Show it why you are traveling forward. If it still won't move out of your way, it means that you have come to a place in your healing path that needs more focus and attention. It means you might need to stay here a little longer and give this particular obstacle more of your thoughtfulness and mindfulness.

13. As you face this challenge as yourself, a few questions to find direction on your path. What is this obstacle, and why is it hard for you to get around? Why do you dislike it so much? Have you had this challenge in your path before? What can you do to move forward on your path, even if the obstacle is still there or shows up again?

14. [allow some time for reflection and meditation]

15. After you have answered some of these deeper questions, you may feel ready to move forward on your healing path, or you may feel like you need to stay here in this space and continue to ask questions where you are. The point is that you are creating awareness on your path of healing. There will always be obstacles, some bigger and more challenging than others. You may find it easier to simply acknowledge what the obstacle is and continue on foot, down the path of your day, until you feel ready to face the challenge when you are ready.

16. Before you release the image of your path and return to your focused daily life, try to picture something else on this journey. Take a deep breath in, filling your body with fresh oxygen, hold the breath for a moment, and then gently exhale, letting it all go. Again, inhale slowly, and exhale slowly. One more time, inhale...hold...and exhale slowly.

17. Now, what is at the end of your path? When you started walking on this path in your mind, did you know what would be at the end of it? Did you even think about what you wanted to be at the end of this long road? If you didn't, it's okay. The purpose of this meditation is to help you

follow your path and know what your obstacles are. Take a moment now to visualize what is at the end of the road for you. What are you walking toward every day? What do you want the end goal to be? Where do you want the journey to lead you?

18. [allow for several moments of reflection and meditation]

19. Now that you have found your end goal, you have a purpose for getting down the path, for understanding and overcoming your obstacles, for choosing a healing journey. The power of visualizing what you want helps you get there faster. When you are working so hard to recover from illness or injury, emotional wounds, mental suffering, it can be easy to lose patience. Whenever you feel doubt, visualize that idea that is at the end of your path. Put yourself back in that space where you can see it clearly and decide exactly how you want to get there. Awaken to your healing path, and you will discover the beauty at the end of the road, somewhere over the rainbow.

20. [allow for a few moments of reflection]

21. Connect to your breath again and let all of your cares and worries drop away. Use your breath to help you focus on your

recovery and healing discovery. As you move forward through your day, imagine what is at the end of your path. You will get there. May you feel rejuvenated and refreshed, relaxed and calm, soothed and loved

Conclusion

Thank you for listening to *Guided Meditation for Pain Relief: Mindfulness to Help Physical and Mental Pain, Take Control of Your Depression, Anxiety, PTSD, Addictions, Injuries, Headaches, Back Pain, Arthritis and More*. All of your time spent listening to these guided meditations and healing practices have already begun to help you heal from the inside out.

The journey is not over, and you will find that working with your meditation practice daily is what will help you to take control of your pain relief for good. It will only work if you use them often to help support your recovery and healing process. It takes time and dedication to overcome pain, and these simple and straight forward guided mindfulness practices are easy to use and create long-lasting change on a much deeper level.

As you gain more practice with these materials, you may want to continue with them in a new way. Try using more than one meditation in a session so that you are getting a bigger impact on your pain relief and recovery. Find the ones that seem to help you the most in certain or specific situations and put them together to create a whole long healing session for yourself.

Remember that if you are in need of medical assistance, please contact your health care professional to give you aid and assistance as needed. These helpful meditations are meant to be used in collaboration with other health practices you are in need of. They are a beautiful compliment to the whole healing journey.

Continue with your meditations every day. Trust that your path to relief is in your hands and that a little bit goes a long way. If you have found this information beneficial and relieving, please feel free to leave an honest review of this audio on Amazon. Take care, and may you heal mindfully.